The Power of a Woman:
Classic Soul

Seventeen great Soul hits for women to sing.

Wise Publications
London/New York/Sydney/Paris/Copenhagen/Madrid/Tokyo

Exclusive distributors:
Music Sales Limited
8/9 Frith Street,
London W1D 3JB, England.

Music Sales Pty Limited
120 Rothschild Avenue
Rosebery, NSW 2018,
Australia.

Order No. AM968308
ISBN 0-7119-8608-8
This book Copyright 2000
by Wise Publications

Compiled by Nick Crispin
New music arrangements by Derek Jones
Music processed by Paul Ewers Music Design

Printed in Malta by Interprint Limited

Your Guarantee of Quality
As publishers, we strive to produce every
book to the highest commercial standards.
The music has been carefully designed to
minimise awkward page turns and to make
playing from it a real pleasure. Particular care
has been given to specifying acid-free,
neutral-sized paper made from pulps which
have not been elemental chlorine bleached.
This pulp is from farmed sustainable forests
and was produced with special regard for the
environment. Throughout, the printing and
binding have been planned to ensure a
sturdy, attractive publication which should
give years of enjoyment. If your copy fails to
meet our high standards, please inform us
and we will gladly replace it.

Music Sales' complete catalogue describes
thousands of titles and is available in full
colour sections by subject, direct from
Music Sales Limited.
Please state your areas of interest and send a
cheque/postal order for £1.50 for postage to:
Music Sales Limited, Newmarket Road,
Bury St. Edmunds, Suffolk IP33 3YB.

www.musicsales.com

B.A.B.Y.

Words & Music by Isaac Hayes & David Porter

Verse 2:
Baby oh baby
You look so good to me baby
Baby oh baby
You are so good to me baby.

Just one look in your eyes
And my temperature goes to high
I'm weak for you and can't help it
You know I really don't want to help it.

B.A.B.Y…

Verse 3:
I said baby oh baby
You look so good to me baby
Baby oh baby
How I love for you to call me baby.

When you squeeze…

Anyone Who Knows What Love Is (Will Understand)

Words & Music by Judith Arbuckle, Jeannie Seeley, Randy Newman & Pat Sheeran

just don't know,   no—— they just don't know,——   un-til they've real-ly loved.

fade

Ah———— un-til they've tried love out one time.

Verse 2:
I feel so sorry
For the ones who pity me
Cos they just don't know
No they don't know
What happiness or true love can be.

I know to ever let you go
Oh, is more, is more than I could ever stand
Oh, but anyone
Anyone who knows what love is
Honey will understand.

Don't Make Me Over

Words by Hal David
Music by Burt Bacharach

1. Don't make me ov-er,——— now that I'd do a-ny-thing for you.

Don't make me ov-er,——— now that you know how I a-dore you.

D.%. al Coda

⊕ Coda

Repeat to fade

15

Feeling Good

Words & Music by Leslie Bricusse & Anthony Newley

Free time

N.C.

1. Birds fly-ing high, you know how I feel.___ Sun in the sky,___

you know how I feel.___ Breeze drift-ing on___ by,___ you know how I feel.___ It's a

new dawn, it's a new day, It's a new life___ for me.___ Yeah, it's a new dawn, it's a new day.___ It's a

Verse 3:
Stars when you shine, you know how I feel
Scent of the pine, you know how I feel
Freedom is mine, and I know how I feel
It's a new dawn, it's a new day
It's a new life for me.

For Your Precious Love

Words & Music by Arthur Brooks, Richard Brooks & Jerry Butler

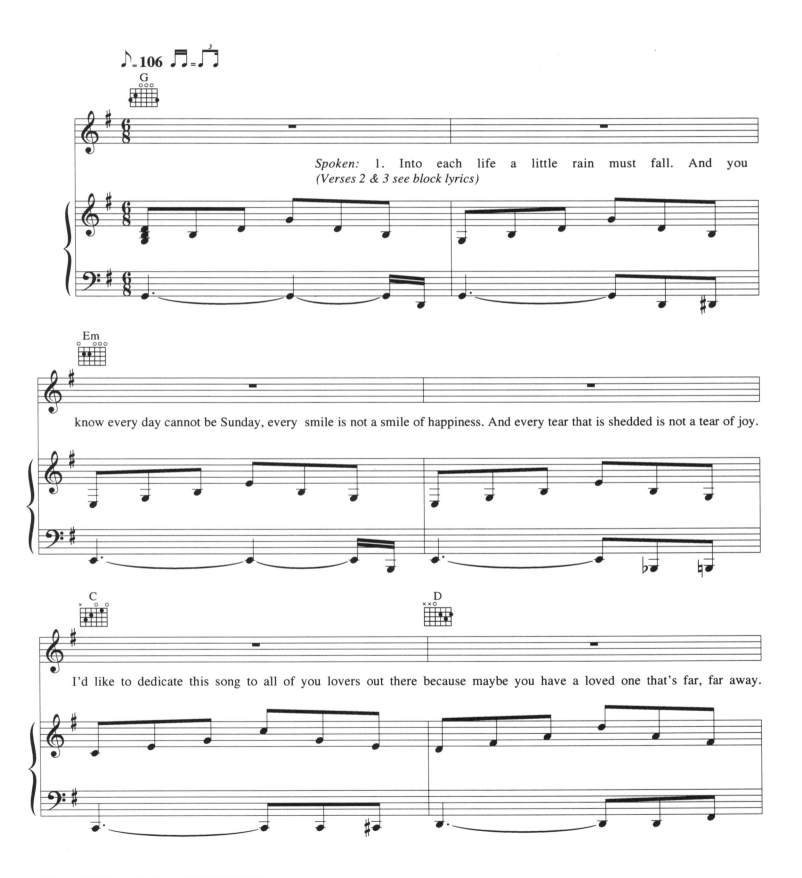

Spoken: 1. Into each life a little rain must fall. And you
(Verses 2 & 3 see block lyrics)

know every day cannot be Sunday, every smile is not a smile of happiness. And every tear that is shedded is not a tear of joy.

I'd like to dedicate this song to all of you lovers out there because maybe you have a loved one that's far, far away.

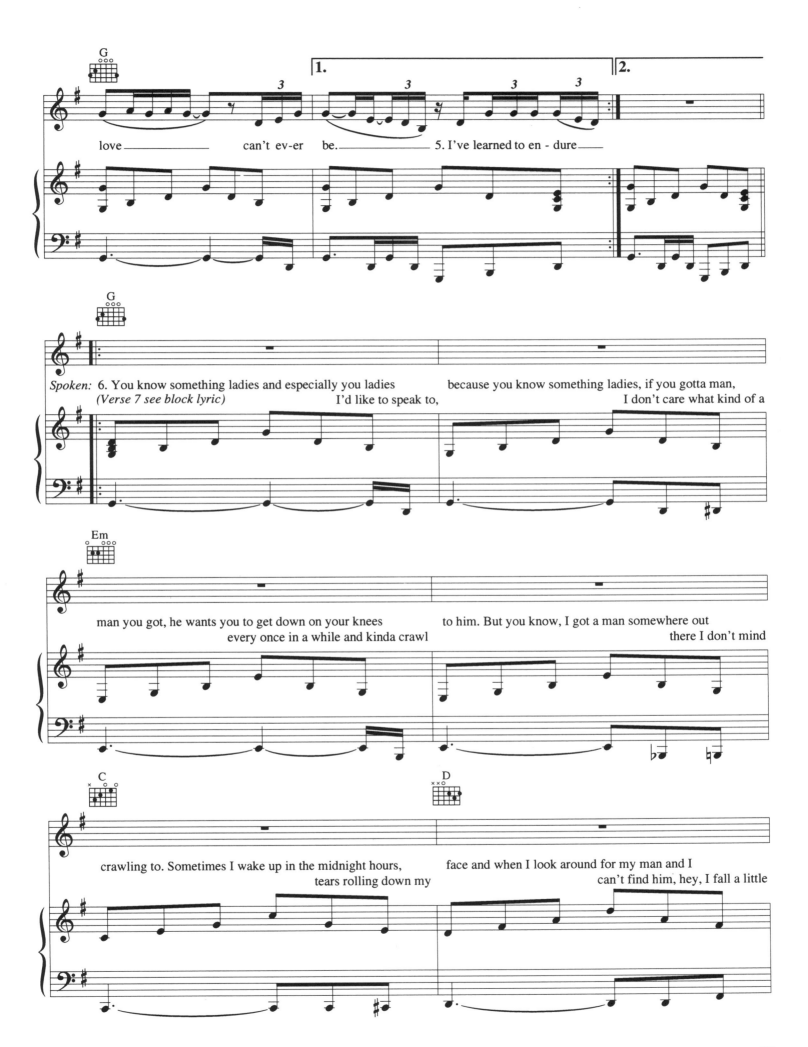

love _____ can't ev-er be. _____ 5. I've learned to en - dure _____

Spoken: 6. You know something ladies and especially you ladies *(Verse 7 see block lyric)* I'd like to speak to, because you know something ladies, if you gotta man, I don't care what kind of a

man you got, he wants you to get down on your knees every once in a while and kinda crawl to him. But you know, I got a man somewhere out there I don't mind

crawling to. Sometimes I wake up in the midnight hours, tears rolling down my face and when I look around for my man and I can't find him, hey, I fall a little

tell my man that I love him. Yes I will.— Oh.—

Verse 2: (Spoken)
You know, I can imagine when you're all alone in the wee wee hours of the night
Why don't you get yourself a piece of paper and a pencil and sit down
And, Lord have mercy, decide to write
Knowing all the time that this letter that you write may not be a comfort to your loved one
But let me tell you something you can say
You can say "Darling, for your precious love, I give you the world on a silver plate"
Huh, but you know as well as I that you'd be telling a great big lie
And you don't wanna do that to your loved one
Neither would I.

Verse 3: (Spoken)
But you can say "Darling, for your precious love I'd climb the highest mountain"
You know something ladies and gentlemen
You could even go out as far a telling him or her that you'd try to swim the deepest sea
But I think if you always sit back, relax, put your mind at rest and listen to me
I think I can give you a better understanding of what I'm trying to say, mm.

Verse 5:
I've learned to endure, oh and I
…wanted you…
Lady…
I was so lonely… and so blue
Good God am I, messed when I found you.

Verse 7:
But sometimes I think He don't even hear me
So I have to fall a little lower on my knees, look a little higher
Kinda raise my voice a little higher
And this is what sing when I call for my man
I expressly want you ladies to listen to me because maybe you can try this
It might help you every once in a while
This is what you sing when you call on your man
Learn to endure.

Verse 9:
With your friends and mine
There's nothing in this whole wide world I wouldn't do for you darling
No, and I won't go
Lord I gotta see my baby again
I gotta tell my man that I love him
One more time.

Go Now

Words & Music by Larry Banks & Milton Bennett

Verse 2:
We've already said, so long
I don't want to see you go
But boy you had better
Go now, go now
Go now, go now
Don't you even try

Bridge 2:
To tell me that you really don't
Want to see it in this way now.
Don't you know
If you really meant what you said
Darlin', darlin', darlin'
I wouldn't have to keep on begging you
Begging you, begging you
Begging you to stay.

Go now *etc.*

Have A Little Mercy

Words & Music by Dorian Burton & Clyde Otis

1. I nev-er ev-er thought I would live —— to see the day ——

that I'd —— be run-ning af-ter a man —— this way. ——

2. Babe,
(Verse 3 see block lyric)

when-ev - er you're out of my sight all I do is pace the floor,———

my nerves are nev-er set-tled un - til you walk_ through my door.———

At night_ when I'm lay-ing in bed—— all I do is toss and turn———

and if you don't light-en up on me my life———— will be ru - ined. Have a lit-tle

mer - cy on__ me ba - by, show a lit - tle mer - - - cy, ooh ba -

- by, just a lit - tle bit, show me some__

1.

mer - cy.__

2.

Show me some_ mer - - - cy babe, have a lit - tle

mer - cy on__ me babe, I need your__ mer - - - cy, I'm beg-ging you for

mer - cy, I'm on my knees ba - by, I'm beg-ging you for mer - cy.

Verse 3:
Now you got me falling on my knees
And eating right out of your hands,
I'm right here to fulfil your desire
And every command.
Now what more could you ask for
When you got a fool like me,
I'm getting what I deserve
Cos I'm where I want to be.

Have a little mercy on me babe
Show me some mercy
Just a little bit
Show me some mercy
Mercy.

How Was I To Know You Cared

Words & Music by Jerry Williams Jr. & Gary Bonds

but all you talked a-bout was you.____ Tell me how
(How, how was I to

know you cared.) how was I to know____
(How, how was I to know you cared.)

2. We did-n't have____ too much____ in com - mon,
(Verse 3 see block lyric)

at least that's the way____ it seemed.____
You were nev-er en -

36

of you.   Now— you tell me that   you care,—

I could-n't leave him   cos   it would-n't be   fair.———

D.%. al Coda

✠ *Coda*

Strings

know you   cared.)

Verse 3:
You see the man loves me now
Like you say you do
He's told me of all the sweet things
That I always wanted to hear from you.

Tell me how *etc.*

I Say A Little Prayer

Words by Hal David
Music by Burt Bacharach

live with-out you would on-ly mean heart-break for me._____

me._____ My dar-ling, be - lieve me, for me_ there is no one_____ but

you. Please_ love me too._____

Verse 2:
I run for the bus, dear
While riding I think of us, dear.
I say a little prayer for you.
At work I just take time
And all through my coffee break time
I say a little prayer for you.

I'd Rather Go Blind

Words & Music by Ellington Jordan & Billy Foster

1. Some-thing told____ me it was ov - - - er, (Yeah___)
(Verse 2 see block lyric)

Verse 2:
I was just sitting here thinking
Of your kiss and your warm embrace
When the reflection in the glass
That I held to my lips now babe
Revealed the tears that was on my face.

I would rather be blind *etc.*

Killing Me Softly With His Song

Words by Norman Gimbel
Music by Charles Fox

Verse 2:
I felt all flushed with fever, embarrassed by the crowd
I felt he found my letters and read each one out loud
I prayed that he would finish but he just kept right on.

Strumming my pain with his fingers *etc.*

Verse 3:
He sang as if he knew me in all my dark despair
And then he looked right through me as if I wasn't there
But he just kept on singing, singing clear and strong.

Strumming my pain with his fingers *etc.*

Midnight Train To Georgia

Words & Music by Jim Weatherly

leav-in'___ (leav-in') on___ that mid-night train__ to Geor-gia.(Leavin' on that mid-night train.__)

Yes, said he's go-in' back (go-in' back__ to find) to a sim-pler

place and time. Oh yes he is. And I'll__ be with him (I know you will__
(When-ev-er he takes that ride__ guess who's gonna be right by__ his side.__)

____) on___ that mid-night train to Geor-gia. Hey.
(Leav-in on the mid-night train__ to Geor-gia, woo woo!)

Verse 2:

He kept dreamin' that someday he'd be the star
(A superstar, but he didn't get far)
But he sure found out the hard way
That dreams don't always come true
So he turned all his hopes
And he even sold his old car
Bought a one-way ticket back to the life he once knew.

He's leavin' *etc.*

Nutbush City Limits

Words & Music by Tina Turner

D.%. al Coda

4. No

⊕ Coda

Nut - bush ci - ty,   Nut - bush ci - ty li - mits.

62

Verse 3:
You go to fields on weekdays
And have a picnic on Labour Day
You go to town on Saturdays
And go to church every Sunday.

They call it Nutbush *etc.*

Verse 4:
No whisky for sale
If you get drunk no bail
Salt pork and molasses
Is all you get in jail.

They call it Nutbush *etc.*

Fade out:
A one horse town
You have to watch
What you're putting down
In old Nutbush, oh Nutbush.

Rescue Me

Words & Music by Carl Smith & Raynard Miner

1. Res - cue me or take me in your arms, res - cue me, I want your ten - der charms cos I'm a

(Verse 2 see block lyric)

Verse 2:
Rescue me
Come on and take my heart
Take your love
And comfort every part.

Cos I'm lonely *etc.*

Son Of A Preacher Man

Words & Music by John Hurley & Ronnie Wilkins

♩=90

1. Bil - ly Ray was a preach - er's son— and when his
(Verse 2 see block lyric)

dad- dy was preach- ing he'd come— a- long;   when they gath- ered round and start- ed talk - ing

was he was, mm,_____ yes he was._____

1.

2.

How well I____ re-mem-ber

the look that was in____ his eyes,_____ steal-ing kiss-es from me____ on the sly,_____

Verse 2:
Being good isn't always easy
No matter how hard I try.
When he started sweet talking to me,
He'd come and tell me everything is all right,
He'd kiss and tell me everything is all right,
Can't get away again tonight.

Stay With Me Baby

Words & Music by Jerry Ragovoy & George David Weiss

Verse 2:
Who did you touch,
When you needed tenderness.
I gave you so much,
And in return I found happiness.
Baby what did I do,
Maybe I was too good,
Just too good for you.
No no, I can't believe,
You'd really leave.

Stay with me *etc.*

(Take A Little) Piece Of My Heart

Words & Music by Jerry Ragovoy & Bert Berns

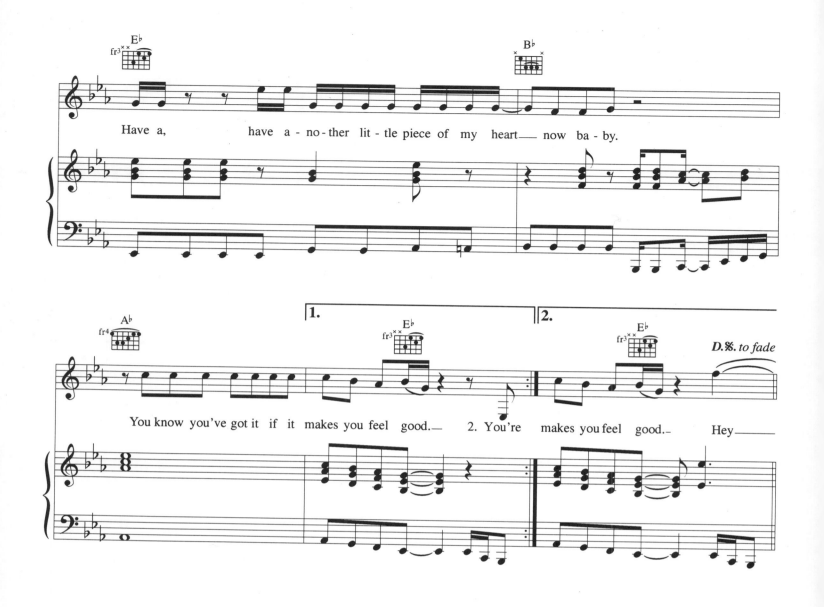

Have a, have a-no-ther lit-tle piece of my heart—— now ba-by.

You know you've got it if it makes you feel good.—— 2. You're makes you feel good.— Hey——

Verse 2:
You're out on the street (looking good)
And you know deep down in your heart that ain't right
And oh, you never hear me when I cry at night
I tell myself that I can't stand the pain
But when you hold me in your arms I say it again.

So come on *etc.*